WHAT IN THE WORLD?

How many insect pictures do you see?
What are they called? What other animals do you see?

1.

2.

3.

4.

5.

6.

Photos by Peach Reynolds

Answer on page 47.

FANCY WEBWORK

Which spiffy spider wove which web?

B

D

F

2

4

6

FIND THE FAKE FLOWER

April the Florist wanted to make a bouquet of two dozen fresh flowers. She only had twenty-three flowers left in her shop. For the twenty-fourth flower she used something else. What was it?

Answer on page 47.

SPACE SHIP AHOY!

Can you help this space-walking astronaut get back to the ship?

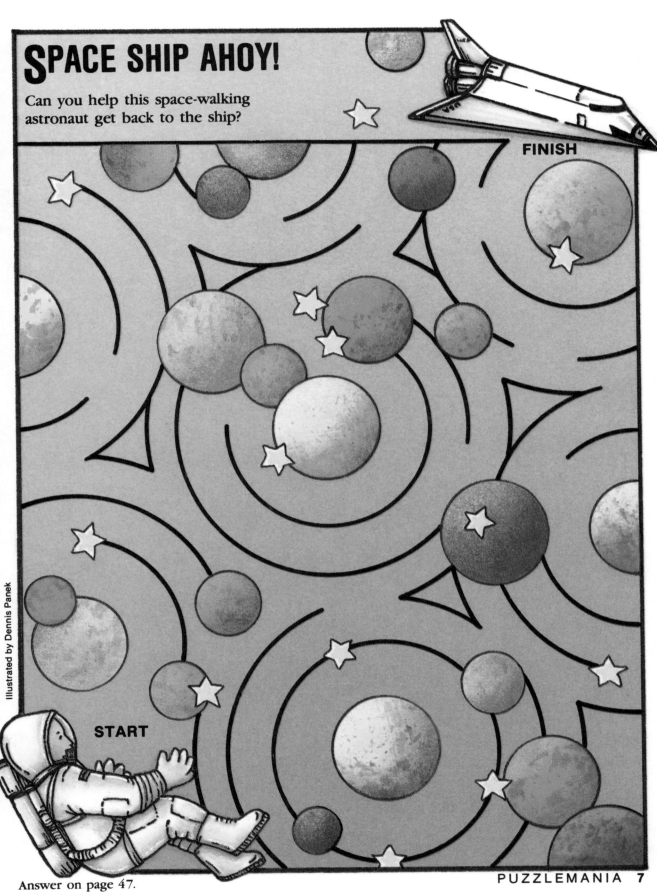

FINISH

START

Illustrated by Dennis Panek

Answer on page 47.

ARE YOU A PET EXPERT?

See if you can answer these tricky questions about pets. If you don't know, take a guess. Some answers may surprise you.

1. People in America own nearly seventy million cats and dogs. Which of these two is the more popular pet?

   A. Dogs
   B. Cats
   C. They are about equal.

2. Your aunt gave you two goldfish for your birthday. Why should you put underwater plants in their bowl?

   A. Plants help the goldfish breathe.
   B. Goldfish eat the plants.
   C. Plants make the bowl look pretty.

3. If you want a pet that talks back, get a parrot. About how many words can a parrot learn to say?

   A. 10
   B. 100
   C. As many as you know

Illustrated by Barbara Gray

4. It's suppertime, and you're out of turtle food. What can you give your turtle to eat instead?

   A. Lettuce and spinach
   B. Raw hamburger
   C. All of the above

5. Your sister found a new pet for you while playing outdoors. It is either a toad or a frog. How can you tell?

   A. Frogs croak and toads don't.
   B. Frogs have smooth, wet skin, and toads have dry, bumpy skin.
   C. There is no difference between the two.

7. Your cousins are bringing their new dog to meet you. Your uncle says it's the most popular breed in America. What is it?

   A. Collie
   B. German shepherd
   C. Poodle

6. You wake up at night and check to see if your tropical fish are sleeping. They are all staring at you. Why?

   A. Fish have no eyelids to close.
   B. Fish never sleep.
   C. You woke them up.

8. A cat depends on its whiskers to help it feel things. Which of these statements is *not* true?

   A. Whiskers help cats move in the dark.
   B. Whiskers can tell hot from cold.
   C. Whiskers help cats fit into tiny spaces.

Answer on page 47.

GROCERY GOOFS

How many things can you find wrong in this picture?

STOP, LOOK, AND LIST

Under each category list one thing that begins with every letter. For example, one state that begins with *C* is Colorado. See if you can name another.

States

C _____

P _____

M_____

O _____

S _____

Pizza Toppings

C _____

P _____

M_____

O _____

S _____

Things with Wings

C _____

P _____

M_____

O _____

S _____

Answer on page 47.

Illustrated by Doug Taylor

TAKE A GOOD LOOK

Agent Double-O is on the lookout for words with two *o*'s in a row. She has already spotted a cook looking at a book. How many double-o words can you find?

Answer on page 47.

MIXED-UP PAINTS

All the mixed-up words in the middle match the artist's paints, but only one is next to the correct color. Unscramble the words to see which word matches the paint.

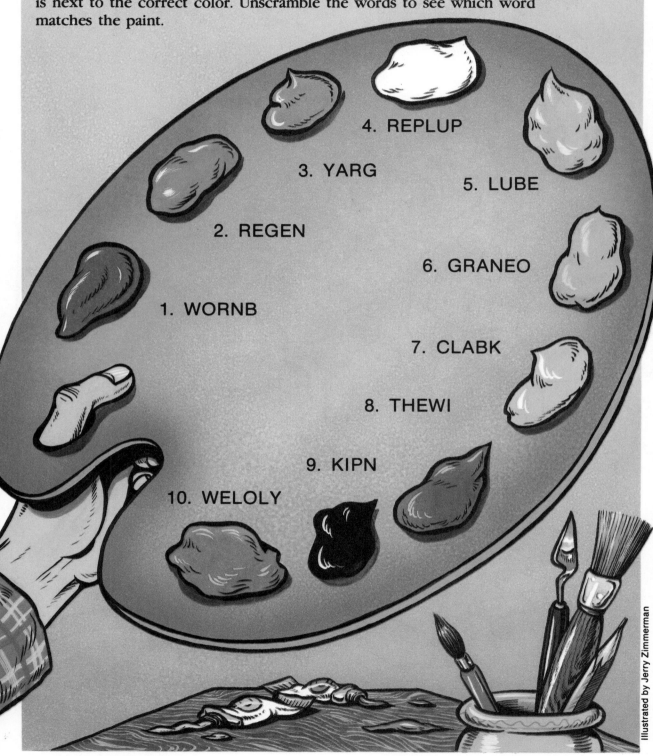

4. REPLUP

3. YARG

5. LUBE

2. REGEN

6. GRANEO

1. WORNB

7. CLABK

8. THEWI

9. KIPN

10. WELOLY

Answer on page 47.

Illustrated by Jerry Zimmerman

MISSING MIDDLE

Michael carved four figures on his totem pole. Use your imagination and fill in the two that are missing.

Illustrated by Jerry Zimmerman

THINGAMAJIGS

There are at least six differences between these two . . . whatever they are! Can you find them?

ROW, ROW, ROW

Each house has something in common with the two others in the same row. For example, all three houses in the middle row across are made of wood. Look at the other rows across, down, and diagonally. What's the same about each row of three?

Illustrated by John Nez

Answer on page 48.

MYSTERY WORKER

Who could the items pictured below belong to? To find out,
use the clues to fill in the blanks. Then put the numbered letters
in the answer spaces at the bottom of the page.

A. Royal hat

B. Snow White's seven friends

C. Beanstalk grower

D. Glass footwear

E. Witch's poisoned fruit

F. Queen's charming son

G. Egg from a special goose

H. King's wife

I. Royal palace

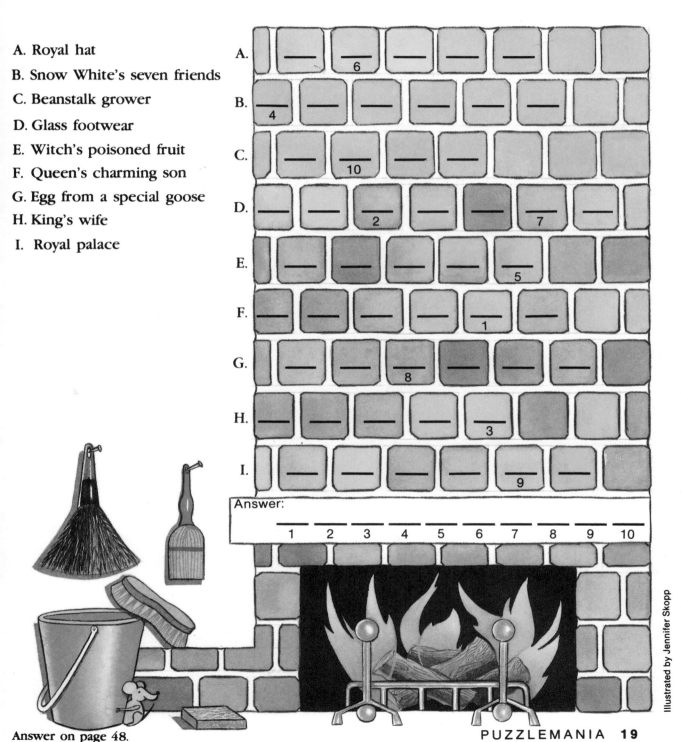

A. _ _ _ _ _ _
      6

B. _ _ _ _ _ _ _
   4

C. _ _ _ _ _
      10

D. _ _ _ _ _ _ _
        2   7

E. _ _ _ _ _
            5

F. _ _ _ _ _
          1

G. _ _ _ _ _ _
      8

H. _ _ _ _ _
        3

I. _ _ _ _ _ _
          9

Answer:
_ _ _ _ _ _ _ _ _ _
1 2 3 4 5 6 7 8 9 10

Illustrated by Jennifer Skopp

Answer on page 48.

CAPITAL CHALLENGE

Find and circle the state capitals in the letters on the next page. Look up, down, sideways, backward and diagonally. Then fill in the names of the states on the list below.

ALBANY, NEW YORK

ANNAPOLIS, M

ATLANTA, G

AUGUSTA, M

AUSTIN, T

BATON ROUGE, L

BISMARCK, N

BOISE, I

BOSTON, M

CARSON CITY, N

CHARLESTON, W

CHEYENNE, W

COLUMBIA, S

COLUMBUS, O

CONCORD, N

DES MOINES, I

DENVER, C

DOVER, D

FRANKFORT, K

HARRISBURG, P

HARTFORD, C

HELENA, M

HONOLULU, H

INDIANAPOLIS, I

JACKSON, M

JEFFERSON CITY, M

JUNEAU, A

LANSING, M

LINCOLN, N

LITTLE ROCK, A

MADISON, W

MONTGOMERY, A

MONTPELIER, V

NASHVILLE, T

OKLAHOMA CITY, O

OLYMPIA, W

PHOENIX, A

PIERRE, S

PROVIDENCE, R

RALEIGH, N

RICHMOND, V

SACRAMENTO, C

SAINT PAUL, M

SALEM, O

SALT LAKE CITY, U

SANTA FE, N

SPRINGFIELD, I

TALLAHASSEE, F

TOPEKA, K

TRENTON, N

Answer on page 48.

```
F E H G Z I H J A C K S O N A T S U G U A
L J R A R E L B S A N T A F E N O T S O B
I I N P R A M C H A R L E S T O N D L J A
T N K A Q T L B M E L A S R N O T N E R T
T D C N F L F E M O N T P E L I E R Y X O
L I R N L A S O I D S L L P N Z Y I I S N
E A A A H N U J R G C F A A O D E N V E R
R N M P H T G E J D H R B N K P E S S J O
O A S O T A M F U B O I S E S E T G A H U
C P I L R D O F N W A C H E C I C P I U G
K O B I O R N E E A W H E L A Y N I N X E
D L P S F O T R A C E M O I R B B G T W N
L I R E K C G S U O E O L N S H C N P Y N
E S O R N N O O T L S N Y C O E O W A A E
I D V R A O M N O U S D M O N L L Q U U Y
F O I E R C E C P M A H P L C E U Y L S E
G V D I F M R I E B H G I N I N M L L T H
N E E P A C Y T K I A H A D T A B W U I C
I R N R L F C Y A L B A N Y C U I O N U
R Z C P H O E N I X L H A R R I S B U R G
P A E I I N O S I D A M E L L I V H S A N
S E N I O M S E D Y T I C A M O H A L K O
```

IT'S CRYSTAL CLEAR

Gaze into this crystal ball, and see how many circles you can find.

Illustrated by Doug Taylor

Answer on page 48.

DOT MAGIC

Connect the red dots from 1 to 136. Then connect the blue dots from 1 to 94. That's a lot of dots, but you're sure to finish with a smile.

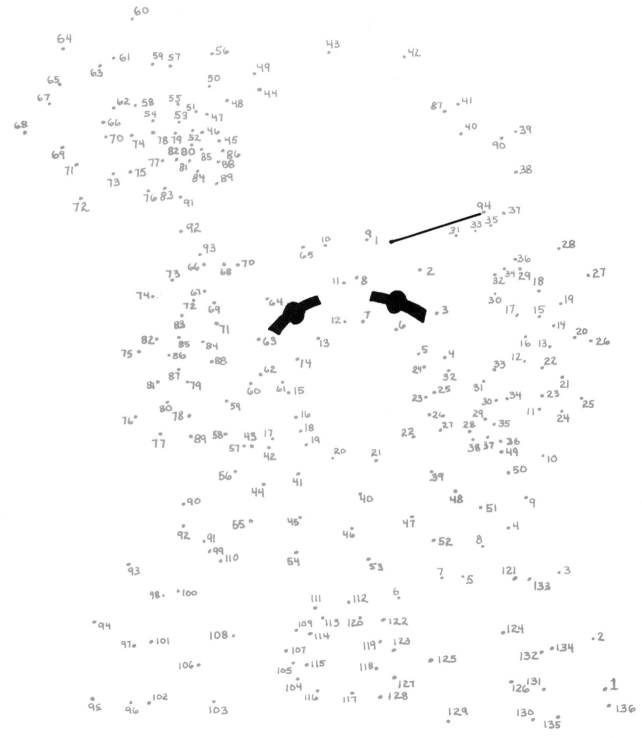

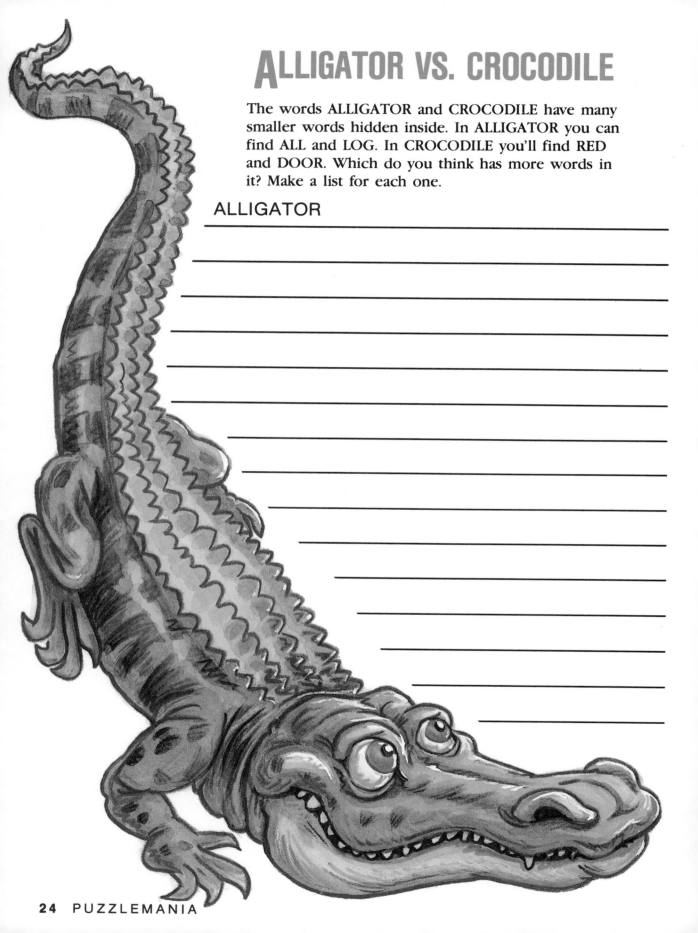

ALLIGATOR VS. CROCODILE

The words ALLIGATOR and CROCODILE have many smaller words hidden inside. In ALLIGATOR you can find ALL and LOG. In CROCODILE you'll find RED and DOOR. Which do you think has more words in it? Make a list for each one.

ALLIGATOR

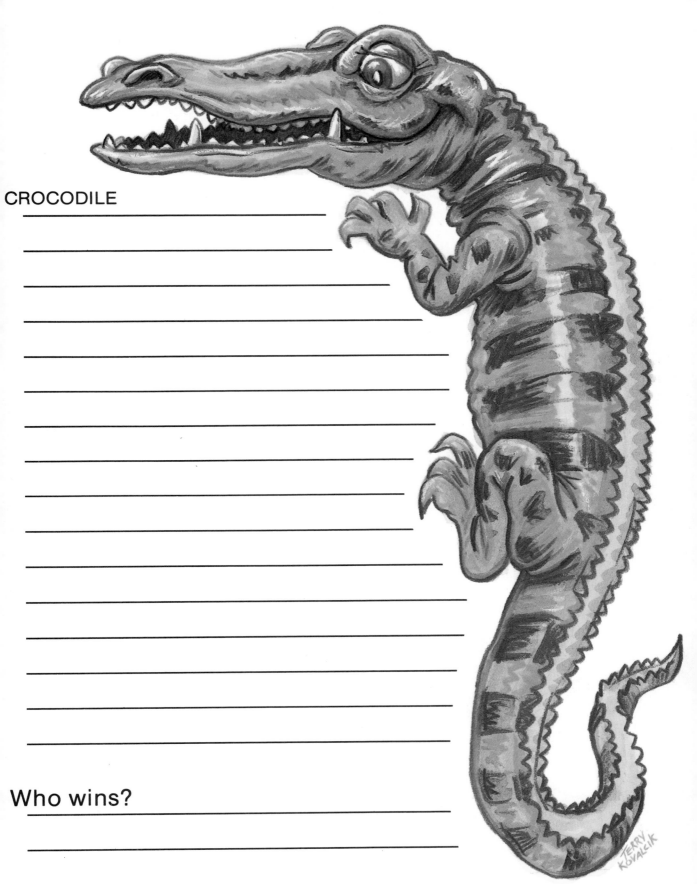

CROCODILE
_____
_____
_____
_____
_____
_____
_____
_____
_____
_____
_____
_____
_____
_____

Who wins? _____
_____

Answer on page 49.

PICTURE MIXER

Carefully copy each part of the picture into the space with the same number on the next page.

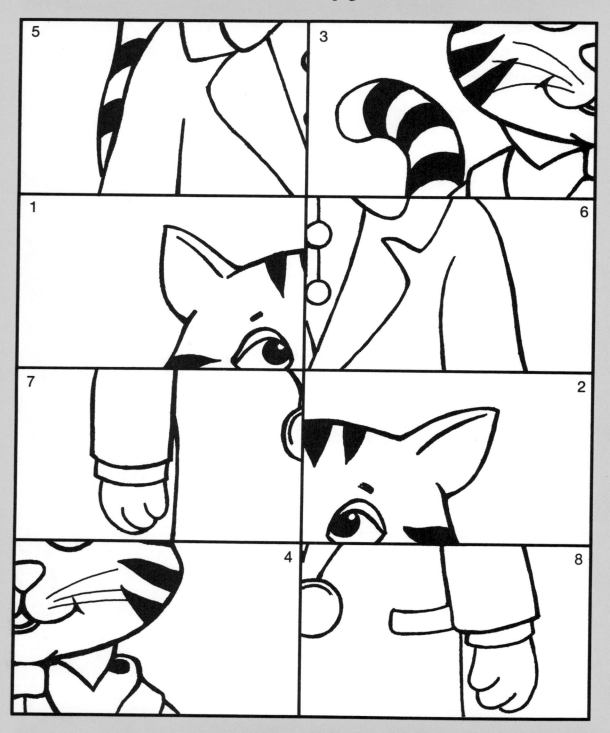

Answer on page 49.

1

2

3

4

5

6

7

8

POSTAL PUZZLER

Follow the directions and pick up a letter at each house you pass. Put the letters in blank spaces at the bottom of the page. When you finish, you'll find out what the stamp said to the envelope.

(Hint: Remember that "right" and "left" depend on the direction you are heading at the time.)

1. Start down Main Street and turn left on Rose Drive.
2. Go left on Short Street.
3. Turn right on Western Avenue, then right again on Walnut Street.
4. Turn left on Little Avenue.
5. At Hemlock Street turn left, then turn right on Western Avenue.
6. Turn right on Maple Street and left on Green Way.
7. At Oak Street make a right.
8. Turn right on Freedom Way. Then turn left at the first street on your left.
9. Make a right on Center Avenue. Then turn left on the second street on your left.
10. Go to Liberty Avenue and turn right, then left onto Main Street.
11. At Eastern Avenue make a left and go to Birch Street. Turn left.
12. Turn right on Liberty Avenue and left on Aspen Street.
13. At Court Way turn right. Make another right on Pine Street.
14. Make a quick right onto Yellow Way and a sharp left onto Eastern.
15. Turn left at the first street you come to. Go straight until you come to Center Avenue.
16. Turn right. Go as far as you can and turn right again.
17. Keep going until you come to Eastern Avenue. Make a left.
18. Turn onto Ash Street. Make a right at North Avenue and a left at Willow Street.
19. Stop at the post office.

Illustrated by John Nez

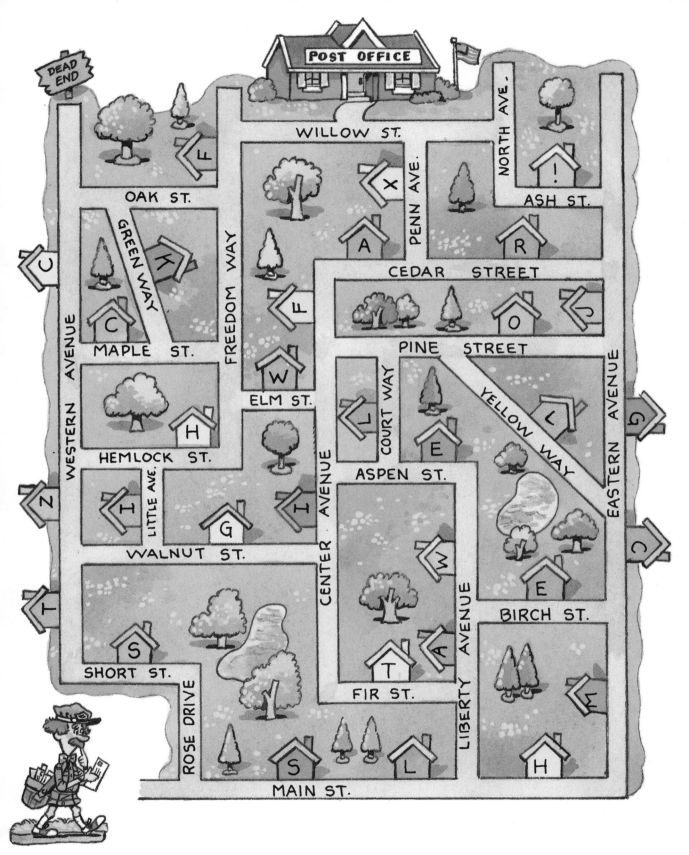

Answer: _ _ _ _ _ _ _ _ _ _ , _ _ _ _ _ !

Where's the pair?

Which two dinosaurs are exactly alike?

Answer on page 49.

PLAYGROUND MEMORIES

Take a long look at this picture. Try to remember everything you see. Then turn the page, and see if you can answer some questions about this playground scene without looking again.

Illustrated by Pat Merrell

DON'T READ THIS UNTIL YOU HAVE LOOKED AT "Playground Memories - Part 1" ON PAGE 31.

PLAYGROUND MEMORIES

Part 2

Can you answer these questions about the playground you saw? Don't peek!

1. How many people were jumping rope?
2. What kind of ball did you see?
3. Was anyone playing hopscotch?
4. How many adults were on the playground?
5. Where did the bird sit?
6. How many girls did you see?
7. Who wore an orange shirt on the slide, a boy or a girl?
8. How many swings were there?

Answer on page 49.

TELL THE TRUTH

Only one of these sentences is true. Which one is it? Can you change one thing in the other sentences to make them true?

1. Spiders have ten legs.
2. Pennies are square.
3. Vanilla ice cream is usually pink.
4. The opposite of night is evening.
5. The alphabet has thirty-six letters.
6. Zebras are covered with spots.
7. The U.S. flag is white, blue, and purple.
8. Peanuts grow underground.
9. Tricycles have four wheels.
10. A, E, K, O, and U are all vowels.

Illustrated by Jennifer Skopp

Answer on page 49.

PICTURE CROSSWORD

These pictures tell you what words to write in the spaces across and down.

Answer on page 49.

Answer on page 49.

FROM THE TORTOISE'S SHELL

In ancient China, stories were sometimes carved on tortoise shells. These stories were written in picture symbols. Each picture symbol, or pictograph, stood for a word or idea. Here are some Chinese pictographs:

⊙ sun   � rain

𝔻 moon   wood

mountain   dog

water   cattle

See if you can read the story:

Early one morning when the ⊙ rose, Li Tsung set out on a journey up the ⩊ . He took his dog and a stick of wood to help him drive the cattle down out of the hills. The dog led the way, and Li Tsung followed.

Li Tsung crossed a stream of water and climbed the mountain . Soon, with the wood and his dog , Li Tsung had gathered all of the cattle . He started down the mountain .

It began to rain . The rain fell very hard. water rushed down the mountain . The water in the stream rose higher and higher. Li Tsung, the dog , and the cattle could not cross the water .

The ⊙ went down and the 𝔻 came out. Li Tsung lay down and slept on the mountain . The next morning, when the ⊙ rose, the water had gone down. With his dog and the wood , Li Tsung crossed the water and led the cattle home.

Answer on page 50.

DEAR TUNA ANNIE

Brendon is learning to type. He tried typing a letter to his aunt. He typed so fast that he scrambled some letters. He laughed when he read it because so many words didn't make sense. Can you fix the mixed-up words?

Dear **Tuna** Annie,
    Kanth you for the nice **stenpers.** The **stráwee** fits perfectly and I love the model **rainaple.** You always **wonk** just what I **kiel**!
    I had a big **tarpy** last week. Ten of my **ifnerds** came over to **yalp** games and eat **drabyhit** cake. We had a really **dogo** time.
    I look **wofdarr** to seeing you next week. Maybe we can play **sniten** or go to the **ozo** the way we did last **remums.**
    Kanths again!
        Love,
        Brendon

Answer on page 50.

Illustrated by Terry Kovalcik

INSTANT PICTURE

There is a sea animal hiding in this ocean of lines and dots. To find it, color every section that contains just two dots.

Answer on page 50.

CROSSWORD FUN

Across

1. Important parts of a fence
4. Miss Muffet _ _ _ on a tuffet.
7. Opposite of in
8. Wish
9. Tiny bit of liquid
11. 1, 1, 1, 1, 1, 1
12. Season after winter
15. December 24th is Christmas _ _ _ .
17. Nine planets make up our solar _ _ _ _ _ _ .
20. What cable shares with table
23. Opposite of wild
24. Leonard's nickname
25. _ _ _ away your toys.
26. A woman in a play

Down

1. A pea's coat
2. Belonging to us
3. Red traffic sign's message
4. Something to sing
5. Gorilla
6. Big quiz
8. Truthful
10. Gift
13. Wall-climbing plant
14. Breakfast, lunch, or dinner
16. Famous story-telling uncle
18. Noisy parts of some dancing shoes
19. Simple Simon _ _ _ a pieman.
21. Beatrice's nickname
22. What clock and locate share

Illustrated by Paul Richer

Answer on page 50.

SEEDS FOR SUPPER

A blue jay, a cardinal, a goldfinch, and a chickadee are at your bird feeder. In the feeder are white, yellow, green, and brown seeds. Each bird likes only one type of seed. Use the clues below to find out which bird likes which seeds.

1. The chickadee does not like the yellow or green seeds.
2. The blue jay does not like the green or white seeds.
3. The goldfinch likes white seeds.
4. The cardinal likes the type of seed that both the blue jay and the chickadee do not like.

Answer on page 50.

Y'S WORDS

Here are twelve words that begin with the letter *Y*.

YAK	YEAR	YESTERDAY	YOUNG
YARD	YELLOW	YET	YOUR
YARN	YELP	YOLK	YAWN

Can you find them hidden among these letters? Look up, down, sideways, backward, and diagonally.

Illustrated by Jerry Zimmerman

Answer on page 50.

SPACE AGE ALPHABET

The name of Crypto's planet is hidden in her alphabet. Where does she live?

The rest of the planets are written with Crypto's alphabet. Use the Super Space Alphabuster to write them with your alphabet.

The name of my planet is hidden in my alphabet. Can you find it?
K L M N O Q S V W X Y
Z J U P I T E R A B C D
E F G H

SUPER SPACE ALPHABUSTERS

Crypto's	Yours	Crypto's	Yours
K	A	U	N
L	B	P	O
M	C	I	P
N	D	T	Q
O	E	E	R
Q	F	R	S
S	G	A	T
V	H	B	U
W	I	C	V
X	J	D	W
Y	K	F	X
Z	L	G	Y
J	M	H	Z

Illustrated by Jerry Zimmerman

6. JOEMBEG

_____

Answer on page 50.

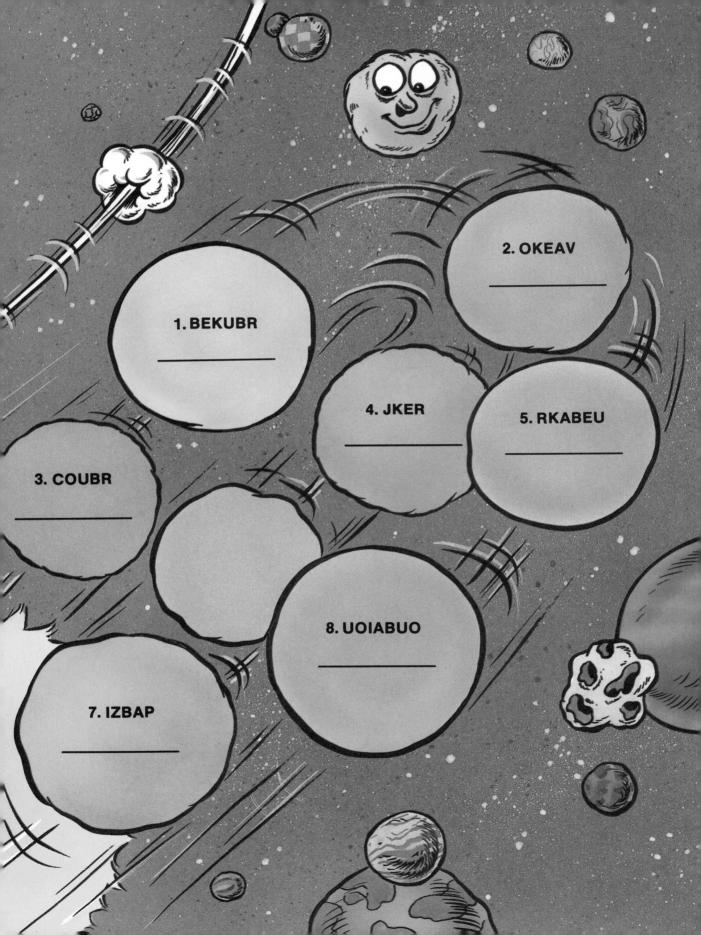

HIDDEN PICTURES

How many objects can you find hidden in this picture?

CONNECTIONS

First connect the black dots from 1 to 70. Then connect the red dots from 1 to 58. Last connect the blue dots from 1 to 23 to make something you might see out in the country. What is it called?

Answer on page 51.

ANSWERS

COVER

WHAT IN THE WORLD (page 3)

1. butterfly
2. giraffe
3. grasshopper
4. geese
5. caterpillar
6. ladybugs

The ladybugs, the grasshopper, the caterpillar, and the butterfly are all insects.

FANCY WEBWORK (page 4)

1. F	3. B	5. D
2. C	4. E	6. A

FIND THE FAKE FLOWER (page 6)

(It's a pinwheel.)

SPACE SHIP AHOY! (page 7)

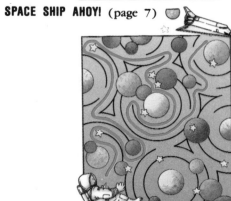

ARE YOU A PET EXPERT? (page 8)

1. A. Dogs are most popular.
2. A. Plants help the goldfish breathe.
3. B. Parrots can learn to say about one hundred words.
4. C. Turtles can eat lettuce, spinach, and hamburger.
5. B. Frogs have smooth, wet skin, and toads have dry, bumpy skin.
6. A. Fish have no eyelids to close.
7. C. The poodle is the most popular breed of dog in America.
8. B. Whiskers cannot tell hot from cold.

STOP, LOOK, AND LIST (page 11)

There are many good answers. Here is one set that works. You may have found others.

States	Pizza Toppings
California	Cheese
Pennsylvania	Peppers
Minnesota	Mushrooms
Oregon	Onions
South Carolina	Sausage

Things with Wings
Chicken
Plane
Moth
Owl
Swan

TAKE A GOOD LOOK (Page 12)

Here are the words we found. You may think of others.

baboon	cuckoo clock	hoop	roof
balloon	door	igloo	scoops
bamboo	food	kangaroo	scooter
book	football	loon	spool
booth	footprints	moose	stool
boots	goose	noon	tools
broom	hood	notebook	tooth
cook	hoof	papoose	wood
cookie	hook	pool	wool

MIXED-UP PAINTS (page 14)

1. Brown
2. Green
3. Gray
4. Purple
5. Blue
6. Orange
7. Black
8. White
9. Pink
10. Yellow

Gray is the only word by the matching paint color.

ROW, ROW, ROW (page 18)

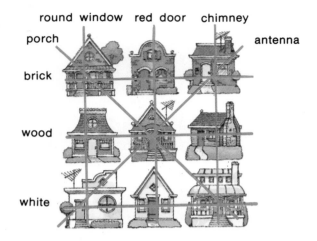

round window red door chimney

porch antenna

brick

wood

white

MYSTERY WORKER (page 19)

A. Crown F. Prince
B. Dwarfs G. Golden
C. Jack H. Queen
D. Slipper I. Castle
E. Apple Mystery Worker: Cinderella

CAPITAL CHALLENGE (page 20)

Albany, New York
Annapolis, Maryland
Atlanta, Georgia
Augusta, Maine
Austin, Texas
Baton Rouge, Louisiana
Bismarck, North Dakota
Boise, Idaho
Boston, Massachusetts
Carson City, Nevada
Charleston, West Virginia
Cheyenne, Wyoming
Columbia, South Carolina
Columbus, Ohio
Concord, New Hampshire
Des Moines, Iowa
Denver, Colorado
Dover, Delaware
Frankfort, Kentucky
Harrisburg, Pennsylvania
Hartford, Connecticut
Helena, Montana
Honolulu, Hawaii
Indianapolis, Indiana
Jackson, Mississippi
Jefferson City, Missouri
Juneau, Alaska
Lansing, Michigan
Lincoln, Nebraska
Little Rock, Arkansas
Madison, Wisconsin

Montgomery, Alabama
Montpelier, Vermont
Nashville, Tennessee
Oklahoma City, Oklahoma
Olympia, Washington
Phoenix, Arizona
Pierre, South Dakota
Providence, Rhode Island
Raleigh, North Carolina
Richmond, Virginia
Sacramento, California
Salem, Oregon
Salt Lake City, Utah
Santa Fe, New Mexico
Springfield, Illinois
Saint Paul, Minnesota
Tallahassee, Florida
Topeka, Kansas
Trenton, New Jersey

IT'S CRYSTAL CLEAR (page 22)
22

DOT MAGIC (page 23)

ALLIGATOR VS. CROCODILE (page 24)

Crocodile was our winner. Who was yours?

CROCODILE

cider	cord	idle	older
clod	cried	idol	or
cod	deli	led	ore
code	dice	lid	red
coil	dire	lie	rid
coiled	door	lied	ride
color	drool	ode	rod
colored	I	odor	rode
coo	ice	oil	
cool	iced	old	

ALLIGATOR

a	girl	oat	tag
ago	goal	oil	tail
ail	goat	or	tall
air	grill	rail	till
all	I	rag	toil
art	it	rat	toll
at	lag	riot	trail
gait	lit	rot	troll
gill	log	roll	

You may have found others.

PICTURE MIXER (page 26)

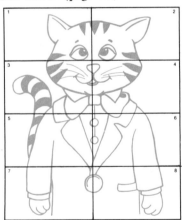

POSTAL PUZZLER (page 28)

What the stamp said to the envelope:
"Stick with me. We'll go far!"

WHERE'S THE PAIR? (page 30)

Dinosaurs 1 and 5 match.

PLAYGROUND MEMORIES (page 32)

1. One person was jumping rope.
2. A boy dribbled a basketball.
3. No one was playing hopscotch.
4. One adult was on the playground.
5. The bird sat on the jungle gym.
6. There were two girls.
7. The boy on the slide wore an orange shirt.
8. There were three swings.

TELL THE TRUTH (page 32)

There may be more than one correct answer. Here are our answers.
1. Spiders have *eight* legs
2. Pennies are *round*.
3. Vanilla ice cream is usually *white*.
4. The opposite of night is *day*.
5. The alphabet has *twenty-six* letters.
6. Zebras are covered with *stripes*.
7. The U.S. flag is *red*, white, and blue.
8. **True,** peanuts do grow underground.
9. Tricycles have *three* wheels.
10. A, E, *I*, O, and U are all vowels.

PICTURE CROSSWORD (page 33)

FISH STORY (page 34)

FROM THE TORTOISE'S SHELL (page 35)

Early one morning when the *sun* rose, Li Tsung set out on a journey up the *mountain*. He took his *dog* and a stick of *wood* to help him drive the *cattle* down out of the hills. The *dog* led the way, and Li Tsung followed.

Li Tsung crossed a stream of *water* and climbed the *mountain*. Soon, with the *wood* and his *dog*, Li Tsung had gathered all of the *cattle*. He started down the *mountain*.

It began to *rain*. The *rain* fell very hard. *Water* rushed down the *mountain*. The *water* in the stream rose higher and higher. Li Tsung, the *dog*, and the *cattle* could not cross the *water*.

The *sun* went down and the *moon* came out. Li Tsung lay down and slept on the *mountain*. The next morning, when the *sun* rose, the *water* had gone down. With his *dog* and the *wood*, Li Tsung crossed the *water* and led the *cattle* home.

DEAR TUNA ANNIE (page 36)

Dear *Aunt* Annie,

Thank you for the nice *presents*. The *sweater* fits perfectly, and I love the model *airplane*. You always *know* just what I *like!*

I had a big *party* last week. Ten of my *friends* came over to *play* games and eat *birthday* cake. We had a really *good* time.

I look *forward* to seeing you next week. Maybe we can play *tennis* or go to the *zoo* the way we did last *summer*.

Thanks again!

Love,
Brendon

INSTANT PICTURE (page 37)

CROSSWORD FUN (page 38)

SEEDS FOR SUPPER (page 40)

The bluejay likes yellow seeds.
The cardinal likes green seeds.
The goldfinch likes white seeds.
The chickadee likes brown seeds.

Y'S WORDS (page 41)

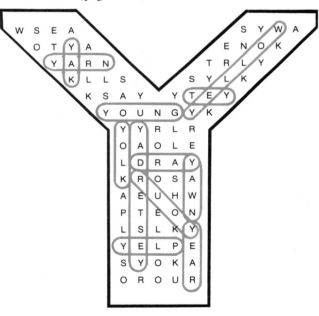

SPACE AGE ALPHABET (page 42)

Crypto's planet: Jupiter

1. Uranus
2. Earth
3. Venus
4. Mars
5. Saturn
6. Mercury
7. Pluto
8. Neptune